WHERE ARE THEY?
SEARCH FOR SUSIE

By
Anthony Tallarico

Incorporated

Copyright © 1990 Kidsbooks, Inc. and Anthony Tallarico
7004 N. California Ave.
Chicago, Ill. 60645

ISBN: 0-942025-97-0

Hardcover edition 1st published in 1990
All Rights reserved including the right
of reproduction in whole or in part in any form.

Manufactured in the United States of America

One day Susie's mom and dad took her to the Big Fun Amusement Park. Susie was excited and couldn't wait to see all the rides. While her parents were buying popcorn, Susie wandered off and started to explore the park.

SEARCH FOR SUSIE IN THE BIG FUN PARK AND...

☐ Banana peel
☐ Bowling ball
☐ Burst balloon
☐ Camel
☐ Candle
☐ Clothesline
☐ Clown-o-saurus (3)
☐ Ducks (2)
☐ Ear of corn
☐ Egg
☐ Football
☐ Ghost
☐ Hearts (2)
☐ Ice-cream cone
☐ Jack-o'-lantern
☐ Juggler
☐ Magnifying glass
☐ Megaphone
☐ Octopus
☐ Pencil
☐ Periscopes (2)
☐ Police (6)
☐ Raccoon
☐ Red wagon
☐ Reindeer
☐ Socks (2)
☐ Sour-puss-saurus
☐ Turtle
☐ Violinist

"Where's Susie?" asked her father.

"I don't know," answered her mother. "But we'd better start looking for her."

Meanwhile, Susie heard lots of shouting and splashing. Everyone seemed to be having fun. Or were they?

SEARCH FOR SUSIE AT THE WATER RIDE AND...

- ☐ Bone
- ☐ Bride
- ☐ Cactus
- ☐ Candy canes (2)
- ☐ Cupcake
- ☐ Curtains
- ☐ Dogs (2)
- ☐ Egg
- ☐ Fire hydrant
- ☐ Fish (4)
- ☐ Flying horse
- ☐ Goat
- ☐ Ground hog
- ☐ Hearts (3)
- ☐ Hobbyhorse
- ☐ Hot dog
- ☐ Island
- ☐ Moby Dick
- ☐ Nightmare
- ☐ Peter Pan
- ☐ Pickle barrel
- ☐ Police-o-saurus
- ☐ Sailboat
- ☐ Sea horse
- ☐ Surfboard
- ☐ Tuba
- ☐ Umbrella

Susie left the Water Ride and headed for the carousel. Around and around it went. Susie thought she heard her parents calling her, but with all the noise and excitement she couldn't find them.

SEARCH FOR SUSIE AT THE CAROUSEL AND...

- ☐ Alarm clock
- ☐ Ball
- ☐ Bat
- ☐ Broom
- ☐ Butterfly
- ☐ Cannon
- ☐ Dancing bears (2)
- ☐ Dentist
- ☐ Ear
- ☐ Fan
- ☐ Frog
- ☐ Golf bag
- ☐ Kangaroo
- ☐ Lamp
- ☐ Lollipop
- ☐ Mushroom
- ☐ Neckties (3)
- ☐ Parrot
- ☐ Pig
- ☐ Roller skate
- ☐ Scarecrow
- ☐ Snake
- ☐ Snow lady
- ☐ Super hero
- ☐ Telescope
- ☐ Top hat
- ☐ Truck
- ☐ Turtles (2)
- ☐ Unicorn
- ☐ Yo-yo

Susie's next stop was the Fun House. Wow! Things were really wild in there! Susie's mom and dad were searching for her in the Fun House too.

SEARCH FOR SUSIE IN THE FUN HOUSE AND...

☐ Banana peel
☐ Barrel
☐ Bib
☐ Cave man
☐ Cup
☐ Football helmet
☐ Headless body
☐ Humpty Dumpty
☐ Igloo
☐ Jack-in-a-box
☐ Jack-o'-lantern
☐ Kite
☐ Magician
☐ Medal
☐ Parachute
☐ Pie
☐ Pillow
☐ Pot
☐ Puppy
☐ Saw
☐ Sled
☐ Snake
☐ Sock
☐ Stool
☐ Susie's parents
☐ Target
☐ Traffic light
☐ Train engine
☐ Wacky clock
☐ Watermelon slice
☐ Wreath

Susie finally found her way through the maze and out of the Fun House. Then she heard loud, squeaking sounds which she followed to a huge, spinning Ferris wheel. "What a neat park this is," thought Susie.

SEARCH FOR SUSIE AT THE FERRIS WHEEL AND...

- [ ] Arrow
- [ ] Astronaut
- [ ] Birdhouse
- [ ] Broom
- [ ] Camera
- [ ] Candy cane
- [ ] Chimney
- [ ] Copycat
- [ ] Dinosaur guitarist
- [ ] Eye
- [ ] Golfer
- [ ] Hammock
- [ ] Hockey stick
- [ ] Ice skates
- [ ] Kite
- [ ] Lions (2)
- [ ] Oil can
- [ ] "Oup and Doup"
- [ ] Painters (2)
- [ ] Papa bear
- [ ] Plumber's plunger
- [ ] Santa Claus
- [ ] Screw
- [ ] Star
- [ ] Surfer
- [ ] Susie's parents
- [ ] Telephone
- [ ] Ticket collector
- [ ] Umbrella
- [ ] Watering can

Susie couldn't resist a ride on a roller coaster. Even an old, rickety-looking roller coaster. She bought a ticket and off she went!

SEARCH FOR SUSIE ON THE ROCK AND ROLLER COASTER RIDE AND...

- ☐ Balloons (5)
- ☐ Bat
- ☐ Birdcage
- ☐ Boat
- ☐ Can
- ☐ Carrot
- ☐ Cave man
- ☐ Dino-in-a-bottle
- ☐ Drummer
- ☐ Firefighter
- ☐ Fire hydrant
- ☐ Flames
- ☐ Flower eater
- ☐ Mailbox
- ☐ Moose
- ☐ Mummy
- ☐ Police-o-saurus
- ☐ Rabbits (5)
- ☐ Red tire
- ☐ Rocket
- ☐ Safe
- ☐ Skateboard
- ☐ Skier
- ☐ Sock
- ☐ Tennis racket
- ☐ Tick-tack-toe
- ☐ Unicycle
- ☐ Weights
- ☐ Window
- ☐ Wreath

Meanwhile, Susie's parents were still searching for her.

After a thrilling ride on the roller coaster, Susie needed a nice, quiet place to relax. The Game Room seemed like the perfect spot. Not much was happening there.

SEARCH FOR SUSIE IN THE GAME ROOM AND...

☐ Apples (2)
☐ Baseball
☐ Basketball
☐ Bomb
☐ Boomerang
☐ Can
☐ Candle
☐ Carrot
☐ Coffeepot
☐ Cup
☐ Dice
☐ Donkey's tail
☐ Dracula
☐ Earmuffs
☐ Ghost
☐ Gift box
☐ Graduate
☐ Guitar
☐ Hammer
☐ Horseshoe
☐ Pencil
☐ Poodle
☐ Sailboat
☐ Telescope
☐ Timekeeper
☐ Top hat
☐ Turtles (3)
☐ Umpire
☐ Unicorn
☐ Yo-yo

Susie played a few games, then headed for...

...the bumper cars! What an exciting ride that was! Susie banged and bumped and crashed her way from one end to the other. She waved to her parents who unfortunately got bumped before they could see her.

SEARCH FOR
SUSIE ON
THE BUMPER
CARS AND...

- ☐ Alien
- ☐ Artist
- ☐ Banana peel
- ☐ Birdcage
- ☐ Bride
- ☐ Cactus
- ☐ Camel
- ☐ Candy cane
- ☐ Cans (5)
- ☐ Car "007"
- ☐ Car "8A"
- ☐ Car "54"
- ☐ Cat
- ☐ Crown
- ☐ Fire hydrant
- ☐ Giraffes (2)
- ☐ Hot dog
- ☐ Ice-cream cone
- ☐ Jack-o'-lantern
- ☐ Kite
- ☐ Light bulb
- ☐ Mice (2)
- ☐ Musician
- ☐ Pig
- ☐ Police (2)
- ☐ Shoemobile
- ☐ Speed limit
- ☐ Stars (2)
- ☐ Sunglasses
- ☐ Surfer
- ☐ Target

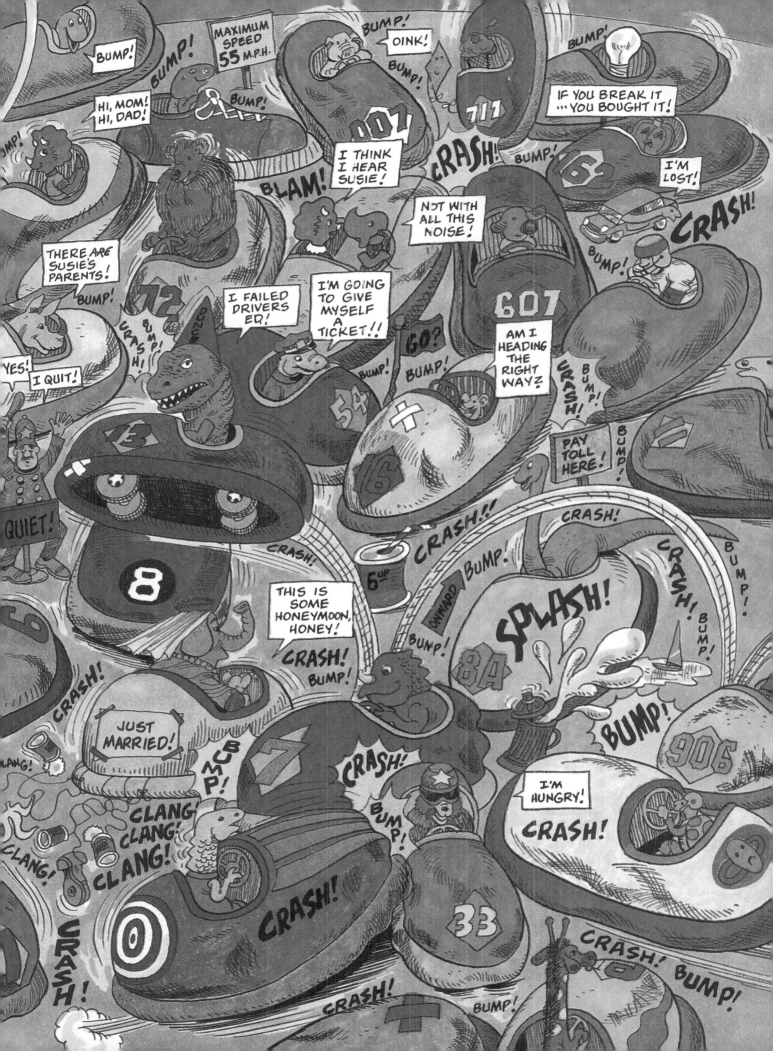

No trip through an amusement park would be complete without a visit to the Haunted House—one of Susie's favorite places.

SEARCH FOR
SUSIE IN
THE HAUNTED
HOUSE AND...

☐ Arrow
☐ Basket
☐ Bats (3)
☐ Belt buckle
☐ Broom
☐ Bumper car
☐ Cheese
☐ Crystal ball
☐ Dragon
☐ Flower
☐ Fly swatter
☐ Hand-in-a-box
☐ Hat on a hook
☐ Mice (4)
☐ Mummy-o-saurus
☐ Mushroom
☐ Owl
☐ Pencil
☐ Pirate's hat
☐ Roller skate
☐ Salt shaker
☐ Skier
☐ Spiders (2)
☐ Spray can
☐ Susie's parents
☐ Turtle
☐ Vulture
☐ Wallet
☐ Witch-o-saurus
☐ Yo-yo

After a long day of fun, Susie was getting hungry. She wondered where she might find a delicious banana split. Then Susie spotted a giant ice-cream cone.

SEARCH FOR SUSIE AT THE ICE-CREAM SHOP AND...

☐ Bad-news lizard
☐ Balloons (3)
☐ Clock
☐ Drum
☐ Eyeglasses
☐ Fish
☐ Fudge pop
☐ Igloo
☐ Kangaroo
☐ King Kong
☐ Mushroom
☐ Paint bucket
☐ Santa Claus
☐ Sled
☐ Slice of pie
☐ Snail
☐ Socks (2)
☐ Sombrero
☐ Spoon
☐ Teeth
☐ Telescope
☐ Tepee
☐ Tire
☐ Top hat
☐ Toy duck
☐ Toy train
☐ TV set
☐ Umbrella
☐ Unicorn

Mom and Dad were still searching and searching for Susie. And...

...there she was! On the giant swings! Susie couldn't wait to tell them about all the fun she had in the Big Fun Amusement Park.

SEARCH FOR SUSIE ON THE GIANT SWINGS AND...

☐ Bat
☐ Bell
☐ Birdhouse
☐ Blue sneaker
☐ Bone
☐ Broken ropes (3)
☐ Broom
☐ Bucket of red paint
☐ Candle
☐ Car
☐ Carrot
☐ Chickens (2)
☐ Fish
☐ Football
☐ Fork
☐ Genie
☐ Horn
☐ Human acrobats (2)
☐ Ice-cream cone
☐ Ice skate
☐ Magnifying glass
☐ Paper airplane
☐ Parachute
☐ Scissors
☐ Slingshot
☐ Snake
☐ Soccer ball
☐ Stars (4)
☐ Ticket collector
☐ Top hat
☐ Waiter
☐ Wrecking ball

SEARCH FOR SUSIE   LOOK FOR LAURA   DETECT DONALD   FIND FRANKIE